STEPHEN J. PYNE

America's FIRES

Management on Wildlands and Forests

The Forest History Society is a nonprofit, educational institution dedicated to the advancement of historical understanding of human interaction with the forest environment. The Society was established in 1946. Interpretations and conclusions in FHS publications are those of the authors; the Society takes responsibility for the selection of topics, the competence of the authors, and their freedom of inquiry.

Forest History Society
701 Vickers Avenue
Durham, North Carolina 27701
(919) 682-9319

Library of Congress
Cataloging-in-Publication Data

Pyne, Stephen J., 1949–
America's fires : management on wildlands and forests / Stephen J. Pyne
p. cm.—(Forest History Society issues series)
Includes bibliographical references (pp. 53–54).
ISBN 0-89030-053-4 (paper)
1. Wildfires—United States—History. 2. Forest fires—United States—History. 3. Fire management—United States—History. 4. Forests and forestry—Fire management—United States—History.
I. Title II. Series
SD421.3.P958 1997
363.37'9—dc21

Photo Credits

Cover: Rabbit Creek Fire, August 1994. Photo by Karen Wattenmaker, Boise National Forest

Title page: Dude Creek Fire, June 1990. Photo by Don Rose, Tonto National Forest

FOREST HISTORY SOCIETY ISSUES SERIES

The Forest History Society was founded in 1946. Since that time the Society, through its research, reference, and publication programs, has advanced forest and conservation history scholarship. At the same time, it has translated that scholarship into formats useful for people with policy and management responsibilities. For five decades the Society has worked to demonstrate history's significant utility.

The Forest History Society Issues Series is the latest and most explicit contribution to history's utility. With guidance from the Advisory committee, the Society selects issues of importance today that also have significant historical dimensions. Then we invite authors of demonstrated knowledge to examine an issue and synthesize its substantial literature, while keeping the general reader in mind.

The final and most important step is making these authoritative overviews available. Toward that end, each pamphlet is distributed to people with management, policy, or legislative responsibilities who will benefit from a deepened understanding of how a particular issue began and evolved.

The Issues Series—like its Forest History Society sponsor—is nonadvocacy. The series aims to present a balanced rendition of often contentious issues. The pages that follow document extraordinarily successful twentieth century campaigns to prevent and suppress wildland and forest fires. Ironically, this fire exclusion has altered ecosystems in ways to increase susceptibility to fire and also insect attacks. As the author points out, healthy forests in America require fire.

ADVISORY COMMITTEE

Contents

Illustrations

Acknowledgments

For their help with various requests for information, I wish to thank Joyce Hassell, Ricky Ingram, Connie Stubbs, and Jerry Williams. Special thanks go to Pete Steen and the Forest History Society for the invitation to contribute to this series and for securing the funding to make publication possible.

Overview

Fire has existed on Earth since lightning first struck terrestrial plants amid an oxygenated atmosphere some 400 million years ago. Humans captured fire some 1.5 million years ago and have enjoyed a species monopoly over fire's manipulation ever since. Free-burning fire has been a constant ecological presence on the American landscape.

But its expression has changed, often dramatically, as new climates, new peoples, and new land uses have become predominant. The evolution of an industrial society committed to the controlled combustion of fossil fuels has fundamentally restructured the continent's fire regimes. These reflect global as well as national trends.

- Domestic uses of fire have shrunk to a vanishing point.
- Agricultural burning has declined sharply, and will probably continue to implode.
- The South remains the major region for burning, with over half of the annually burned area from wildfire and roughly 75 percent of all controlled burning. Most of this burning occurs on public land and industrial pine plantations.
- Throughout the twentieth century, an aggressive fire suppression apparatus, organized around the U.S. Forest Service, steadily reduced burned area on federal lands, although at increasing economic and ecological costs. Today there is a maldistribution of burning—too much wildfire, too little controlled fire.
- Over the past twenty to thirty years federal agencies have sought, with limited success, to restore fire to something like its presettlement regimes. The attempted removal of fire has seriously upset many biotas as well as compromised the prospects for future fire protection.
- From roughly 1970 to 1990 the question of fire in wilderness dominated national concerns. More recently alarm over the intermix landscape has

replaced it, along with campaigns to reinstate some sustainable regime of prescribed burning.

— Urban values and industrial technologies largely dictate the perception of fire and the options open to managers. For most of the American public free-burning fire has been demonized; its reintroduction in controlled forms will most likely be limited to special places. Elsewhere, as long as wildlands remain, wildland fire will flourish.

The Great Barbecue

It was, to the thoughtful, not a pretty site. America in 1880 seemed to be burned, burning, or being readied to burn. There were free-burning fires in all regions, for every imaginable purpose, seemingly without ecological rhyme or social reason. Routine underburning in southern pineries thinned the woods into savannas; slash fires in the Northeast and Lake States savaged trees, soils, and settlements, an international scandal; unplowed prairies erupted into a sea of annual flame; the West was a riot of burning from frontiersmen, ranchers, prospectors, sport hunters, railroads, relict bands of Indians, and lightning. When he assembled the reports of correspondents for the 1880 census, Charles Sargent portrayed a kaleidoscopic landscape of flame and smoke, the typical fire geography of a developing nation. Bernhard Fernow, a Prussian-trained forester, denounced the spectacle as one of "bad habits and loose morals."

Sargent's cartographic snapshot contained lacunae—lands without trees and so dismissed from a register of forest fires; lands without people and so uncatalogued in written records; lands simmering with fire but domesticated and absorbed into an agricultural regime that rendered the flames invisible. Those gaps can be chinked with other sources. In 1878 John Wesley Powell published a map of Utah for his *Report on the Lands of the Arid Region of the United States*, long celebrated as a seminal document in the history of conservation. His crews had classified land by four categories—desert, irrigable, forest, and burned. The burned lands proved the largest in area, rising from the grasses that fringed the desert to the rims of the high plateaus. The primary source of fire was local Indian tribes, burning for their traditional reasons. Given time (and not too much of it) the burned area would overwhelm the forest, and with its watershed ruined, the irrigable would regress into desert. The future of the Rocky Mountains, Powell lectured, depended on the stability of their wooded watersheds, and the future of those forests depended on fire protection.

By the time Sargent's map appeared in print, conflagrations continued to immerse the Lake States in a baptism of fire. Only a decade before had the full magnitude of the region's volatile potential become apparent. Railroads pried apart the North Woods to logging and farming, and like the Trans-Amazon highways that splintered 1980s Brazil and the transmigration schemes that cracked open Borneo, immense fires followed. The 1871 Peshtigo holocaust killed some fourteen hundred settlers even as Chicago burned and established an international standard for forest fire disasters, spilling beyond the headlines of staid newspapers and into the pages of *Harper's Weekly* and the *Illustrated London News.* The 1881 sequels in Michigan inspired the American Red Cross to participate, for the first time, in civilian disaster relief. And alerted to what was apparently a new norm the Army Signal Corps, precursor to the civilian Weather Bureau, dispatched Sgt. William Bailey to observe the meteorological phenomena associated with what was even then termed a *fire-storm.*

Supplement these accounts with Franklin Hough's 1882 *Report Upon Forestry*, a vast compendium of correspondence. In America fire never strayed far from forests. There were large woodland fires in Pennsylvania, pastoral fires throughout the tallgrass prairies, even mandatory burning in North Carolina. Having completed a complementary survey of European forestry, Hough, like most educated observers, became appalled, mortified, confused, and angered by the colossal wastage, violence, and apathy of America's fire scene. It was the environmental equivalent to the Gilded Age's other excesses, a literal rendering of V. L. Parrington's characterization of the era as the Great Barbecue.

There are other sources, and a library of written accounts proliferated as conservation became a government duty. Even greater is the testimony of the land itself. Photographs from the Great Surveys (and others) that sprawled over the West bear witness to far-burned landscapes. Critics observed that the land could bear a much greater weight of trees than it had, that fires had pruned and scoured potential woodlands into prairies; and they were right. A century later trees so thronged over fire-protected lands that

[1a]

Figure 1. The Great Barbecue, a sampler. (a) Peshtigo fire, 1871, as represented in *Harper's Weekly* and later the *Illustrated London News*. Often advertised as America's "forgotten fire," in fact Peshtigo is one of the often cited and best documented. (b) Railroad punching north through Michigan, a logged and burned wasteland on all sides. A developing country, the American fire scene resembled that of Brazil and Indonesia today. Courtesy Michigan Department of Natural Resources.

[1b]

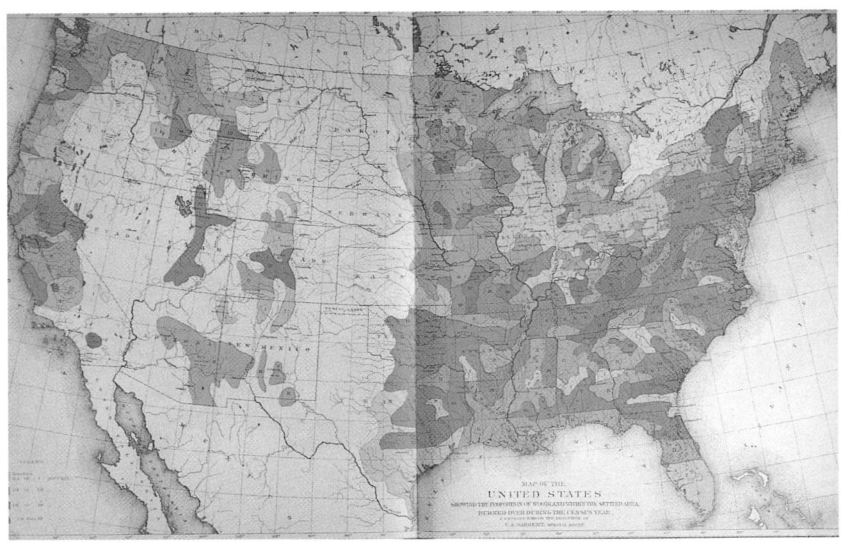

[2a]

they had become a biota far more ecologically degraded than what they replaced.

Clearly the American landscape was fire-flushed and its biota fire-adapted. Yet this could mean different things. It could mean, as an educated elite argued, that nature had accommodated the threat of fire much as bears added a heavy fur coat for winter or trees grew thicker bark. Remove that pressure, and the forest would flourish even better. Nature's adaptations to fire were defensive. So likewise were rural America's social adaptations to riotous burning. To intellectuals, mostly urban, largely attuned to European exemplars and sensitive to civilized criticism, America's smoking landscape was an unconscionable extravagance, an environmental potlatch in which the frontier folk and monopolist robber barons had gleefully heaped the nation's natural wealth onto flames.

Alternatively the scene could mean, as most of the American populace believed, that fire was as inevitable in nature as it was necessary to society, that fire protection was as pointless as the mythical Knut ordering back the tide. Their ancient fire ceremonies proclaimed that fire destroyed evil and promoted good, and in rough fashion that is what they saw happening in their burned fields and woods. Besides, had not Indian burning created the landscapes they most desired? Of course fire could be misused, just as guns and tort laws and theologies could. But to speak of abolishing fire was nonsense.

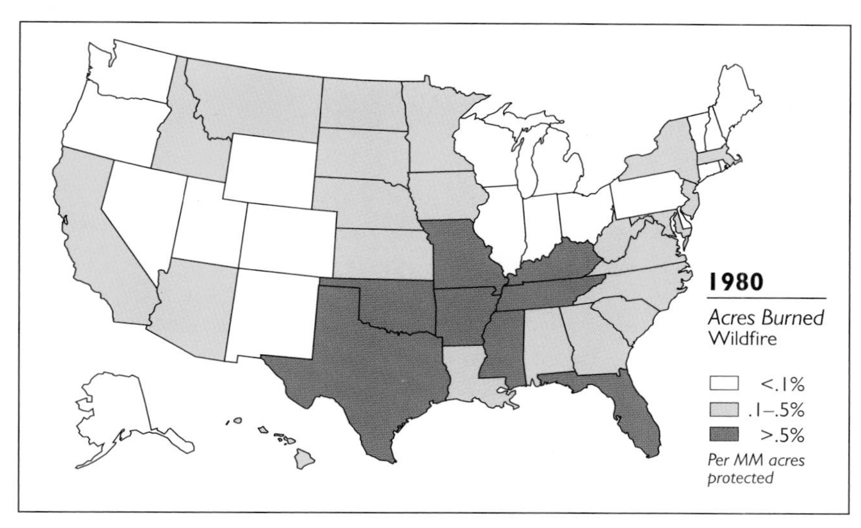

[2b]

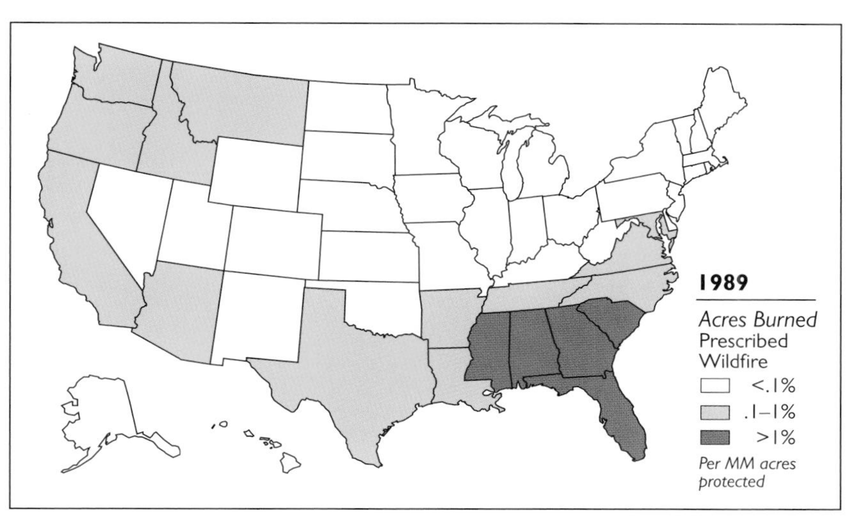

[2c]

Figure 2. The Geography of American Forest Fires. (a) Forest fires, 1880; (b) Wildfire, 1980; (c) Prescribed fire, 1989. Note how the South remains the dominant region for burning, partly for environmental, partly for cultural and political reasons. The magnitude of recent fire in the Great Plains is unusual, and reflects drought conditions. *Sources:* C. S. Sargent, *Report on the Forests of North America (Exclusive of Mexico)*, Vol. 9, Tenth Census of the United States (1880) (Government Printing Office, 1884); U.S. Forest Service, *Wildfire Statistics* (1980); and Ward et al. (1993).

Forest Service Chief Gifford Pinchot later captured the prevailing folk attitude precisely:

> I recall very well indeed how, in the early days of forest fires, they were considered simply and solely as acts of God, against which any opposition was hopeless and any attempt to control them not merely hopeless but childish. It was assumed that they came in the natural order of things, as inevitably as the seasons or the rising and setting of the sun.

No one seriously considered a third perspective, that fires were ecologically necessary. The concept was meaningless in a context in which public lands were being sold, bartered, or otherwise disposed of as rapidly as possible, and where there existed only one nature reserve of any substance, Yellowstone National Park. This hypothetical group would have said, there will be fire, and it is the task of humanity to decide what form it will take. But no such group made any such claims. Rather, the prevailing beliefs held that fires were either a nuisance, and the biota had adapted to them as they would to disease, or else fire was a tool that the biota's ample accommodations made all the more useful. Open burning would remain until some superior tool could replace it.

Looking Back: 1780

Sargent's map would have seemed odd but not bizarre to someone a century earlier. Even a casual critic from 1780 would have noted the missing prairie fires, the lost Indians, and the eruption of fire (and fire-catalyzed change) in forests not prone to regular conflagrations, and the presence of fire-driven (and fire-casting) steam engines. Nothing in the world of the American Revolution had anything like the revolutionary force contained in those fire-powered machines by which to reshape an agrarian geography. In 1780 steam had not progressed much beyond mechanical novelty or the pumping of water-clogged mines. By 1880 it was almost universal in its reach if not its grasp.

But mostly the observer would have noted a change in scale. Fires were larger in some areas, smaller in others, and rearranged everywhere. In forests the burning was larger and faster; in prairies, the vanishing fires would be as noticeable by their absence as the vanquished bison. Yet few fire practices would be unrecognizable. The stalwarts of aboriginal and agricultural America remained vigorously on the scene; fires for hunting and foraging, fires for farming, fires for grazing, fires for charcoal and tar, fires for land-clearing and war and protection against wildfire. This was an agricultural landscape, though one whose pace was quickening under the lash of steam. Many frontier fire practices had, in fact, either been learned from American Indians or represented equivalents transplanted from Europe. These were the fire practices that had informed both the Old World and the New since the Neolithic.

So too the principles of fire control would have seemed similar. Surface fires were fought with firelines, tree boughs, wet sacks, and burning out. Large fires were countered by backfires. The surest prevention was a rearrangement of fuels, preferably on a landscape level. Roads, plowed clearings, and closely grazed pastures, all broke up fields of fire. Large fires were an artifact of vigorous settlement and would vanish as wildlands shrank into an oblivion of fields and villages. Above all, routine controlled burning kept an exuberant, fire-adapted flora under wraps. Broadcast burning brought even odd pockets of resistant woods, rough pasture, and abandoned lots into an agricultural hearth. Proper burning was a civic duty. While errors abounded, particularly during eras of rapid migration and land conversion, while Dark Days, catastrophic wildfires, and fatal miscalculations proved all too common, the principles remained clear. Only fire fought fire.

The Fires This Time: 1980

A century later, however, Sargent's map would be almost unrecognizable, like a fire-drill in an age of pocket matches. It would seem to an American of 1980 as alien as the gutted rain forests of East Kalimantan and Rhondonia, as inexplicable as the fired African savannas, as inexcusable as the pastoral fires that swept the central plateau of Madagascar.

Domestic fire was gone from America. Even fireplaces were regulated, and air quality had so deteriorated in the urban conglomerates in which the vast bulk of the population lived that bans were proposed for barbecues, lawn mowers, and leaf blowers. The population no longer tended daily fires in the hearth, stove, or furnace. Home entertainment centers crowded out fireplaces in new homes. Almost the first injunction leveled at children was the warning that fire was harmful, that they should not touch and should never play with it. "Learn not to burn," urban America was instructed.

Agricultural fire was also receding. Intensification meant better utilization; science and industry developed other pyrotechnologies. The fossil fallow of coal and petroleum, burned in engines or distilleries, substituted for the open flame of living biomass. Even where fire remained the soundest and most economical technique, it confronted constant challenges. Grassburning in the Willamette Valley and around Spokane, for example, were banned as nuisances to urban residents. Slash burning was likewise regulated, and reduced, for similar reasons. Only in the South did open burning persist on any scale, and there increasingly for commercial crops like sugar and pine. As America's farm workers shriveled to something less than 3 percent of the total population, generations grew up without personal experience of burning stubble, firing rough pasture, burning out irrigation ditches, putting the annual debris of pruned branches, raked leaves, dried shocks, and dormant lawns to the torch. Americans were urban, suburban, or exurban, not rural. They saw fire, if they viewed it at all beyond the virtual reality of its televised presence, through an urban prism.

Free-burning fire was restricted largely to reserved public lands. These were immense: they constituted a third of the national estate and, though slowly, they continued to expand. The "fire problem" of the United States had become very largely confined to these lands, places over which people guarded or to which they visited but in which they did not in any meaningful way reside or live off. Wildfires remained common enough outside reserves, especially in the South; but such fires proved an artifact of abandoned farmlands and partially converted suburbs and jurisdictional lapses, and would soon become assimilated into a quasi-urban fire protection system. The enduring fire problem resided in those lands that would not be converted, that would remain as wildlands.

Here fires were wildly maldistributed. There was too much wildfire, too little controlled burning. Almost every observer agreed that fire management had become badly unbalanced, that wildfire was a greater threat than ever, that the failure of America's fire strategy threatened the productivity and ecological health of the protected public lands. Where Sargent and his colleagues saw too much folk burning, a century later critics saw too little. Firefighters employed machinery, massed manpower, chemical retardants, satellite surveillance, and computer-projected fire behavior forecasts. Backfires were restricted, so that even in fire suppression fires were removed. Urban values and exurban settlement dominated discourse over what the fire scene meant.

In truth, fire was everywhere in rapid collapse. Probably not 5 percent of the landscape burned that had regularly burned in 1880. What did burn too often raged in catastrophic eruption. Much of the public lands—lands re-

Figure 3. From rural to wildland fire. (a) The reservation of public land; (b) sites of experimentation in adapting fire control from rural landscapes to wildlands (that is, places not permanently inhabited). For much of the West, fire protection became an institution of frontier settlement. Data for (a) from Dana (1956).

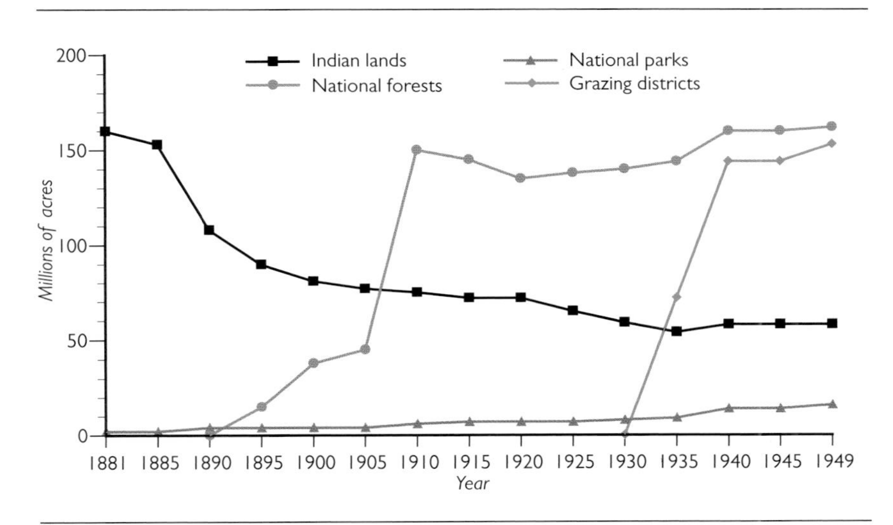

[3a]

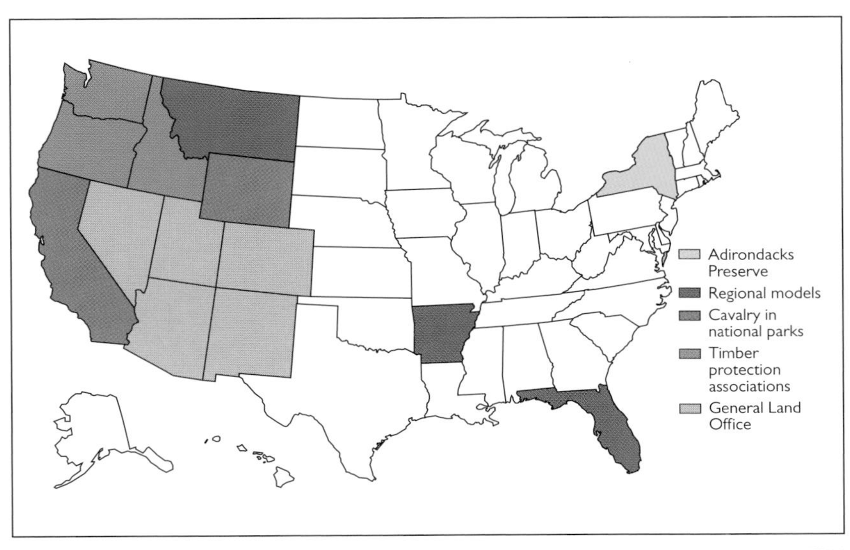

[3b]

served in good measure to protect them from unbridled burning and folk fire practices—wasted away in a fire famine. In counterpoint to Pinchot, free-burning fire (in the abstract) was proclaimed an ecological inevitability, as necessary as rain and sun, while controlled burning, not fire suppression, was considered the first principle of natural understanding and successful management. Everywhere—for different reasons, from different logic—there was a growing consensus that the fire scene was a mess and that the threat of wildfire made public wildlands ungovernable.

After a century of immense labors, an observer from 1980 could share with a counterpart from 1880 only a perplexing unhappiness with their existing fire scenes.

The Great Transformation

It was an extraordinary state of affairs. Industrial combustion technologies had promised to complete humanity's dominion over fire. Instead wildfire was worse than ever. Why could not fires be expunged? Why could not scientific knowledge, political will, modern technology, and public enthusiasm crush fire? If humans could create incendiary devices capable of shattering whole cities, why could they not invent fire-retarding countermeasures of commensurate magnitude? Or, alternatively, if fires were useful and essential, then why were they condemned, and why could they not be safely handled?

Begin with nature. The Earth is a fire planet. For four hundred million years it has had the requisite ingredients to sustain fire—an oxygenated atmosphere, terrestrial fuels, lightning-kindled ignition. Since then fire has remained an evolutionary force, an ecological presence, and in places an indispensable dynamic in the planet's biotic history. The patterning of natural fire regimes follows the cycling of wet and dry conditions. A site must be wet enough to grow fuels and dry enough to ready them for burning. A wet-dry cycle can crack open a biota as a frost-thaw cycle can shatter rock. In some places this cycle repeats annually; in others, over decades or even centuries. But everywhere this dialectic of wet and dry synthesizes into fire regimes. The Earth will burn.

Then consider humanity. *Homo sapiens* is a fire creature, with a species monopoly over fire's manipulation. The geography of Earthly fire has increasingly become the geography of anthropogenic fire. Humanity can, within limits, control both ignition and fuels. *Homo* can start fires, stop fires, rearrange combustibles, substitute domesticated for wild fire, rewire the biotic hardware of fire regimes.

In fact, most anthropogenic fire practices mimic or build upon natural processes. But fire is an extraordinarily interactive technology, and humans can create powerful synergies by felling, ringbarking, grazing, sowing, pruning, digging, transplanting, moving species, and otherwise rearranging fuels and the patterns of fire. They have done this wherever possible. And they have done it for thousands and, in places, for tens of thousands of years. The Earth's fire regimes are unintelligible without their human firebrands.

Certainly, precolumbian peoples exploited fire as fully as their cognate cultures have everywhere else. In the Far West, a well defined wet-dry seasonality allowed fires to wedge into and across most landscapes. In the Rockies, fire-wielding tribes laid down a matrix of burned landscapes within which lightning had to operate. Even in the absence of agriculture, California and Great Basin natives restructured their complex biomes with fire, including the oak savanna that was so characteristic of the Coast Range. With broadcast fire tribes on the Great Plains sustained the tallgrass prairie. In the South swidden agriculture, assisted by uplands burning, began to redefine a landscape mosaic centuries before European contact. Fire-fallow cultivation had penetrated selectively to the Great Lakes and was still expanding northward through New England at the time of contact. The America that Europeans encountered had, in fact, been baked in a hominid hearth for a good ten thousand years.

Colonization replaced one regime with another. Since many of Europe's own fire practices resembled those of America's natives, or soon merged with them, the torch was transferred, an exchange of fire that still left the landscape well tempered by anthropogenic flame. But there were differences, too, beginning with the introduction and extinction of species. Pyrophytes were transported to the New World; some indigenous flora and fauna were exterminated, or driven into enclaves; and diseases reordered human demographics almost overnight. Connections with global markets and capital helped to drive settlement and to determine the patterns it inscribed on the land.

Of special note was the introduction of livestock, since North America had no domesticated fauna apart from dogs and turkeys. As in Eurasia, a fire-pastoral alliance could penetrate landscapes otherwise more or less immune to regular burning. Livestock could open up lands lacking in well-defined fire seasons, just as Neolithic herders had done amid the great shade forests of temperate Europe. The impact became imponderable when immense herds swarmed over the semi-arid West, cropping off grasses and crushing fire.

Forestry and the New Fire Triangle

For fire history, however, the critical events were three, all evident by the latter nineteenth century. Together they inscribed a new fire triangle for the Earth. First, the industrial revolution encased fire within machines and excavated, from the geologic past, new fuels to combust in those mechanical hearths. Fire practices everywhere increasingly felt the competition of these novel technologies for harnessing fire. Internal combustion replaced open burning in field after field of endeavor.

Second, modern science progressively declared itself the oracle and arbiter of fire. The magic of flame was deconstructed into the oxygen-chemistry of combustion. Ancient practices—constraints as well as powers—were dismissed as rural inertia and dangerous superstition; the burning of the woods to cleanse it of ticks and blight seemed no different than burning witches. Folklore had to compete with natural philosophy; folk fire practices with the precepts of academic *philosophes*. The Enlightenment even endowed an engineering corps to oversee open burning. With immense consequences, this role fell to foresters. The ecology and economics of fire would increasingly be viewed through the prism of central European forestry.

But why foresters? That resulted from the third germinal event: the creation by European civilization, expanding its dominion and perceptions over much of the world, of public land reserves, relatively empty of inhabitants. In the United States this shift first took the form of national or state parks such as Yellowstone and the Adirondacks, but in 1891 it came to include vast forests from lands in the public domain not yet patented. This was a historic anomaly, a grand accident; the land was largely vacated of its indigenous peoples, but not yet refilled by settlers. At a stroke these reservations remade the fire geography of America and confirmed the importance of forestry in the political economy of land management.

In fact, the reserves proved part of colonial experiments occurring simultaneously elsewhere in the European imperium. India was the first test for Britain; Algeria, for France; but both stumbled because the local populations were never really removed or controlled, and the lands experienced wave after wave of incendiary fire. Instead the experiments more or less succeeded in those places where, as in America, the lands were temporarily vacant. Thus truly cognate landscapes only appeared in a handful of countries, all colonized by Europe, all momentarily depopulated; these include Canada, Australia, New Zealand, and Asiatic Russia. Increasingly free-burning fire in the developed world focused on just such sites.

These lands demanded fire protection. But having excluded settlers, officials had excluded traditional means of fire control (and fire use). Not living on the land themselves, only guarding them, the forestry brigades that oversaw these invented landscapes interpreted fire protection in terms of fire suppression. Besides, academic forestry, betraying its agronomic origins, condemned fire as superstitious, slovenly, wasteful, primitive. Fire burned humus, which it regarded as the universal index of forest health; fire was the ancient ally of swidden farmers and transhumant pastoralists, the traditional enemies of high forestry; free-burning fire's foes were forestry's friends. Over and again, public debates broke out over colonial fire policy. While intellectuals and the officials who ruled over reserves like proconsuls argued for fire control, even abolition as far as possible, field personnel and natives wanted to base protection on fire use.

All this developed after 1880, and at first the sheer multiplicity of invented lands prompted a rash of experiments. New York grafted wildland fire protection onto rural fire mechanisms. Florida and Arkansas tried to incorporate some elements of controlled burning and thus co-opt folk practices. California sought to adapt frontier fire habits to the needs of timber companies. The Northwest proposed to control free-burning fire and to restrict slash burning on private lands. The national parks enlisted the cavalry to suppress fires as it would a hostile tribe. The likely prospect was that forest fire management would splinter into hundreds of local jurisdictions as education and health care did, that it would be woven into the fabric of American life and landscape, a red thread in a complex plaid.

That did not happen, not on the public lands. A critical decision occurred in 1905 when the Transfer Act moved responsibility for the forest reserves from the General Land Office, which saw its mission as custodial, to the Bureau of Forestry, which (renamed as the Forest Service) took a more aggressive stance. With control over the national forests, forestry now had a political base; with Gifford Pinchot, its charismatic chief, it had a leader of national stature; and with the invigorated Forest Service, the conservation movement had a Progressive Era exemplar of a technocratic bureau serving the public interest. Both the Forest Service and its critics saw fire protection as a visible index of achievement and failure. Within five years, the agency faced a defining crisis. The creation of a national system of wildland fire protection dates from the Great Fires of 1910.

The summer's trial by fire—seventy-eight firefighters dead, more than five million acres of national forests alone burned, a smoke pall that spread from the Rockies to the Great Lakes, staggering debts—traumatized the young Forest Service. The fires were the first great crisis faced by a new chief, Henry Graves. They became the defining moment for two future chiefs, William Greeley and Ferdinand Silcox, both of whom personally weathered the fires in the northern Rockies. Fire heroics by Edward Pulaski and Joe Halm created an instant folklore. Not until this entire generation had passed away—not until the 1940s—would the Forest Service consider fire as anything but an enemy to be fought. "Smoke in the woods," as Greeley put it, became the "yardstick of progress" for American forestry.

Still, there were dissenters. Even as the fires raged that August, a public debate commenced over appropriate fire practices and policies. From California, in particular, a counter-movement—light burning—emerged to argue that the most suitable strategy of fire protection was to copy the "Indian way" and conduct "light burns" that would keep fuels low, the brush pruned, and insects at bay. Others agreed, including Richard Ballinger, then secretary of the interior. But the Forest Service fought back, armed with academic science and the presumptions of Progressive conservation. By the early 1920s light burning was officially condemned as anathema, dismissed as forestry's equivalent to circle-squaring and perpetual-motion machines. Meanwhile the Weeks Act of 1911 allowed the agency to expand by purchase into the eastern U.S., and provided, through cooperative fire protection, a mechanism by which to transfer federal standards to the states. It even allowed the states themselves to organize compacts for mutual firefighting. The fires, the controversy, and the legislation became the forge, the hammer, and the anvil of a national system of fire protection.

Firefight as Moral Equivalent of War

But there was more. During the same August as the Big Blowup, William James, a Harvard professor and one of the architects of Pragmatism as a formal philosophy, published his valedictory essay, "On the Moral Equivalent of War." A pacifist, James was alarmed at the growing militarism he witnessed in the society around him, a martial mania that would end a few years later in the trenches of the Great War. Why not, he argued, redirect that en-

[4a]

Figure 4. Major fires, east and west. (a) Oregon's Tillamook Burn in 1933 charred 240,000 acres, with major reburns in 1939 and 1945; (b) Virginia's Great Dismal Swamp fire in 1930, a time when the entire eastern seaboard burned

[4b]

[4c]

extensively; (c) The scene two decades after Washington's Yacolt Burn of 1902, which was really a complex of fires that covered more than 650,000 acres. FHS photo collection.

[5a]

Figure 5. Great Fires, Light Fires: 1910. (a) The War Eagle Mine in northern Idaho, where Ranger Edward Pulaski led his crew to (relative) safety and subsequently invented both a handtool and a legend; (b) Henry Graves, soon to be chief forester during the 1910 crisis, contemplating light-burning in the Black Hills; (c) Firefight as moral equivalent of war. Courtesy U.S. Forest Service.

[5b]

[5c]

thusiasm to useful purposes? Why could there not be a moral equivalent to war as there was a mechanical equivalent to heat? Why not undertake a national conscription of youths to begin a war on nature, as a displaced surrogate for that waged against other humans? It is unlikely that anyone on those summer firelines read William James, but they shared a common culture. Soon afterwards Theodore Roosevelt urged on his fellow citizens a "life of strenuous endeavor." America would hear other calls to arms; but wildland firefighting became an early and true test of the Jamesian proposal and through it tapped a reservoir of moral fervor. As the cause of conservation needed fire, so fire control needed a cause. Revealingly, Forest Service archival records on fire begin with the body count of the 1910 conflagration. The firefight would endure as America's conceptual prism for interpreting its bold experiment.

The early battles raged in the trenches of frontcountry forests. Here values at risk were high; here light burners and systematic fire protectionists could go head-to-head. But the bulk of the national forests and other public lands lay in more remote landscapes. Whatever their desires, the means at hand checked officials from pursuing those burns with the same intensity. Their staffing and funding restricted agencies' effective fire control to accessible landscapes; and a constant balancing of means and ends was accordingly reflected in a fire policy that balanced the investment in fire control with the values actually at risk. The backcountry—inaccessible, untapped, degraded—burned.

Then, with the ascendancy of the Franklin Roosevelt administration, the backcountry broke open, not only that unroaded landscape in the public domain but those festering environments cut over and abandoned for which fire protection was desirable but without economic justification. The New Deal's conservation largesse (particularly the Civilian Conservation Corps) instantly brought the burning backcountry into the foreground. Almost overnight, it created the means by which to project fire control everywhere. An infrastructure for fire protection emerged that would have taken decades otherwise, or might never have developed at all. In 1935, as an "experiment on a continental scale," Chief Forester Silcox promulgated the 10 A.M. policy, which stipulated control of a fire by 10 A.M. the morning following its report. To pay for this trial by fire, the Forest Service expanded its off-budget forest fire fund to include presuppression as well as suppression. "Emergency" monies sustained the system.

The great smoke plumes rising from the Matilija, Tillamook, and Selway fires formed, to planners, the forestry equivalent of the black soil blown from the Dust Bowl. Burned-over stumplands and over-burned savannas were the ecological analogue to sharecropped cotton fields and marginal wheat farms. The Great Depression manifested itself in America's land as fully as in its factories and cities. There were needs that seemed to defy laissez-faire capitalism, that the federal government could alone afford and oversee. The state sponsored fire protection as it did social welfare and rural electrification. Constructing trails, erecting lookouts, and sending CCC boys to firelines were analogues to social security, welfare subsidies to the needy, and farm price supports. The old equilibrium of means and ends shattered; the means were so great that they compelled new ends to which they might be put. The 10 A.M. policy committed the federal government to universal fire protection that would continue long after the crisis had passed.

World War II reinforced these trends. The public saw fire as weaponry, as blitzed cities, as sabotage, and, thanks to *Bambi* (released in 1942), as a form of ecological murder. Towering convection columns were likened to the fireballs over Dresden and Hiroshima. The crisis of war replaced the economic emergency of Depression. Equally, the American population moved to cities and suburbs, for which fire was threatening, or at most better confined to barbecues. Fire remained as a hostile force; the Cold War confirmed the image of firefighting as an act of national defense. The transfer of surplus military hardware after the Korean War led to an efflorescence of equipment adaptations for fire, most spectacularly the development of the air tanker. Firefighting quickly mechanized. The 10 A.M. policy remained in force, as did most other New Deal institutions. Burned area plummeted.

Fire Famine: From Critique to Crisis

But criticisms mounted, then became irresistible. By 1978, a century after John Wesley Powell published his damning map of the Utah firescape, the federal agencies had reformed their official policies in the hopes of reintroducing more fire. Economics argued that fire suppression had passed a point of diminishing returns. Contemporary ecology insisted that fire had a role in natural or quasi-natural systems; that its eradication could destabilize landscapes and allow fuels to stockpile to the point of detonation. Environmental politics rewrote agency charters, pivoting about America's fascination with wilderness. What began as an incongruity—suppressing lightning fires in nature reserves—became an anomaly. As stresses built, the tectonic plates of federal programs ruptured. Paradigms shifted. Policy changed.

But apart from some symbolic demonstrations, practice did not. The federal agencies continued to do what they were paid to do: they suppressed fire. The amount of land prescribe-burned was small, overwhelmingly concentrated in the South and elsewhere increasingly problematic. It was easy to repudiate the past; tough to impose a future. The Yellowstone conflagrations of 1988 showed just how difficult that task would be. To the public, the fires announced a philosophy almost two decades old; to the fire community, they confirmed the difficulty of managing wildland fire as myth or ideology. Fire was not a philosophical thesis. If fire suppression was insupportable, so too natural fire was inadequate. Even in the wild, humans remained the keeper of the flame. Even in wilderness, even in postmodern America, they would have to do what they had done all their existence as a species. They would have to tend those fires.

In retrospect, the tragedy of American fire history was not that wildfires were suppressed but that controlled fires were no longer set. The downward trajectory of burned area became, in reality, the measure of a fire deficit. The pursuit of fire abolitionism was a chimera. What was required was a change in fire regimes, a reorganization of fires applied and fires withheld. The fire

[6a]

Figure 6. Fields of Fire: The Gains. (a) This U.S. Forest Service smokejumper represents the rapid strike force capabilities that caused acres burned per year to plummet. Even more effective was the surge of road construction that opened up the national forests in the decades following World War II. Forest Service Photo; (b) Most of the reduction in burned area resulted from the establishment of first-order fire

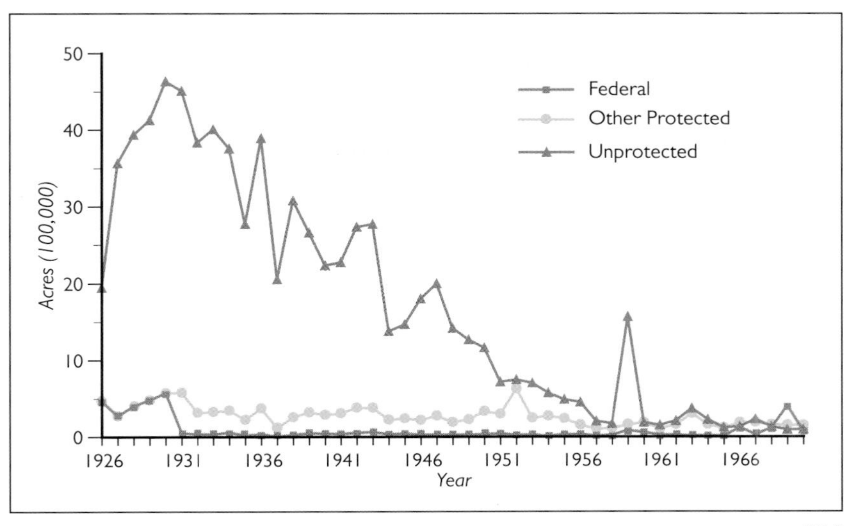

[6b]

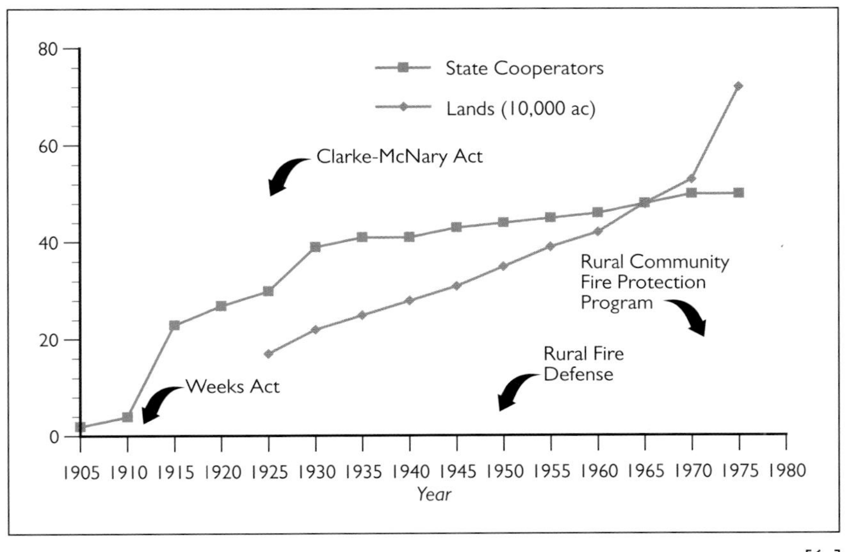

[6c]

protection programs. As more lands came under formal protection, burned area plunged. (c) Cooperative fire programs were a primary mechanism for expanding fire control beyond the dominion of the national forest. The process continues today through various alliances within the intermix fire zone.

[7a]

Figure 7. Fields of Fire: The Costs. (a) A Sikorsky Skycrane enabled rapid deployment of heavy equipment, but at a very high operating cost. FHS Photo Collection; (b) Fire control increasingly had its costs: more and more equipment and personnel went to keep the lid on wildfire. Costs escalated, partly from inflation, largely from the

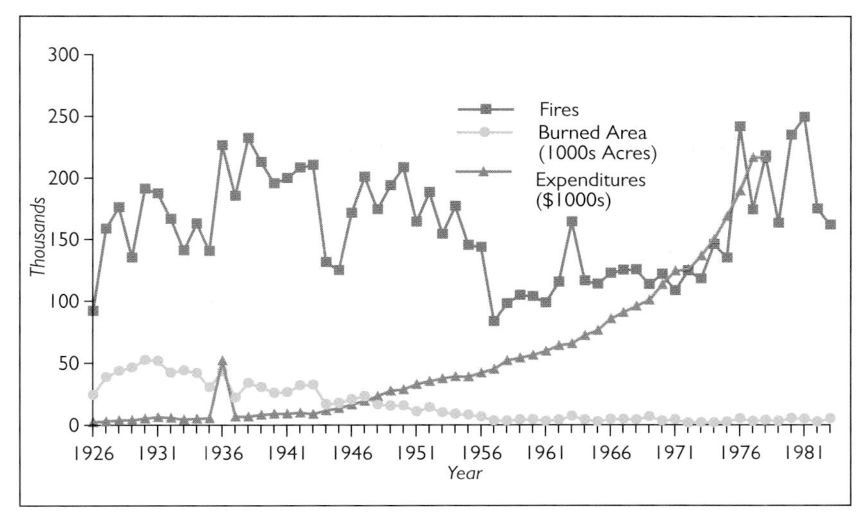

[7b]

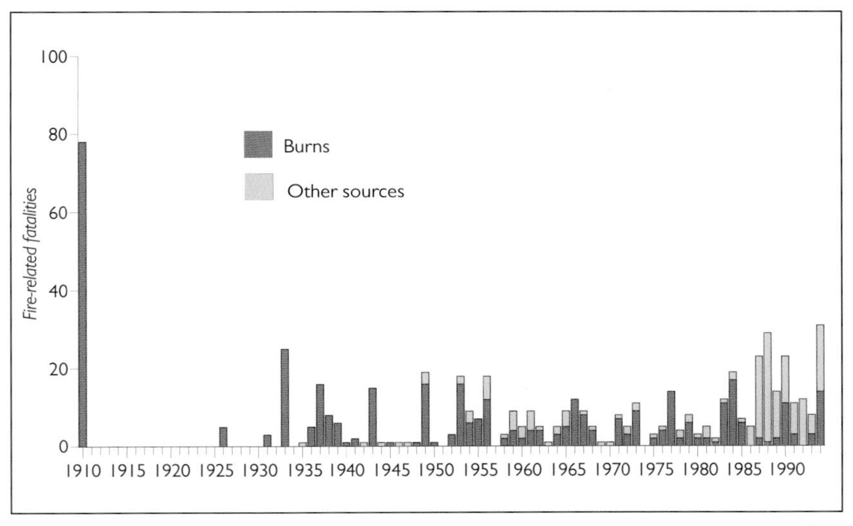

[7c]

increased expense of suppression. (c) Firefighter fatalities, which refuse to fade away. After the 1994 season OSHA censured the federal agencies for failure to satisfy even their own standards of workplace safety.

mosaic that had once shaped America had become a mosaic of fire-problem landscapes for which there was no single solution and no simple social or ecological fix.

Under conditions like those nineteenth century America exhibited, fire protection could be enormously (if temporarily) successful. Folk burners were gone, fires in oft-burned landscapes easily contained, while nature had not yet dispensed its combustion antigens. In some environments, suppression could suspend a landscape for a handful of years, and in some, for decades. Within that grace period it was necessary either to convert the land to some other, less flammable form or to install a species of controlled burning. With trivial exceptions, the U.S. did neither. The fire history of the Carolina Sandhills National Wildlife Refuge suggests that an alternative was possible. Here a tumultuous complex of wildfires was beaten down, and then a new regimen of controlled burns cultivated. By the 1990s more area was burned through prescription than had previously burned by wildfire. That, in brief, was the road not taken. America's federal agencies and their state collaborators chose only the first fork and broke routine wildfire, then lost their way in the darkening woods.

By the early 1990s the crisis was widely, publicly admitted. Fire was as much at the core of "forest health" issues as it had been at "forest devastation" and "timber famine" alarms at the beginning of the century. The philosophical battle over fire policy had long passed away. Agencies operated more from bureaucratic momentum than from conviction; even fire crews, for all the passion they invested in their task, did not believe in existing practices. They were (so they said) not putting fires out, only putting them off. Into this cultural cauldron Norman Maclean dropped his dazzling 1992 bestseller *Young Men and Fire*, a meditation on the fatal 1949 Mann Gulch fire in Montana. The book reached a general audience that statistics, academic histories, ecological monographs, and bureaucratic reviews had failed to find. Through it fire connected to an American intelligentsia that had often dismissed wildland fire as a historical freak or as ecological theater from the Wild West like grizzly attacks or reenactments of the shootout at the OK Corral.

Then in 1994 fires walloped the West, vaporized $965 million in (off-budget) suppression funds, incinerated hundreds of houses, and claimed the lives of thirty-two firefighters. An outside observer might well have diagnosed the patient as close to systemic collapse. Bureaucratic CAT-scans and policy autopsies followed. Even professional forestry issued a public *mea culpa* that its

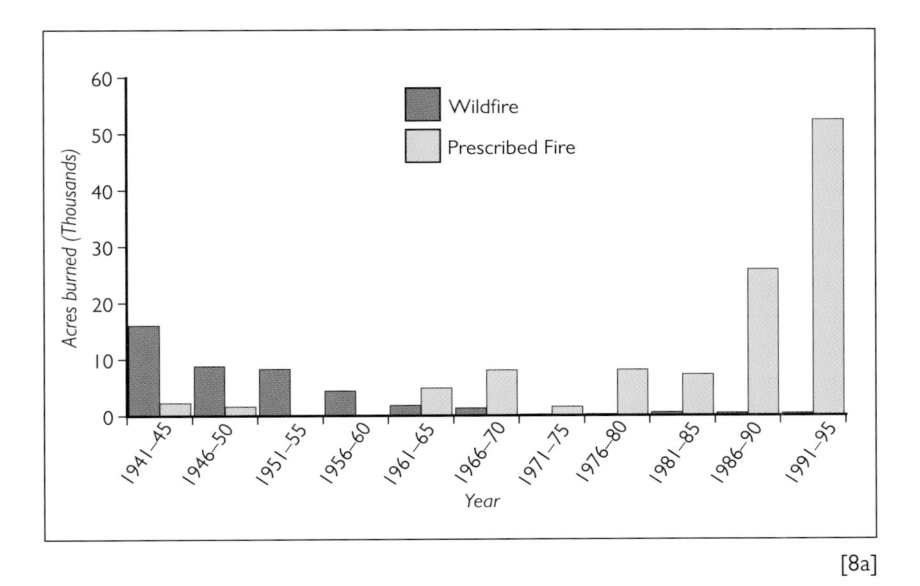

[8a]

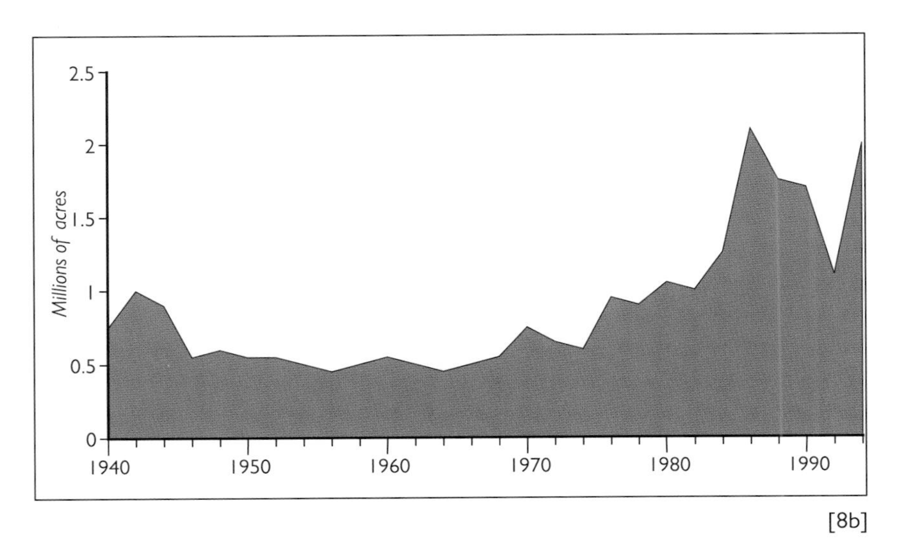

[8b]

Figure 8. Divergent paths: (a) Carolina Sandhills National Wildlife Refuge confronted a wildfire menace, but having controlled it commenced prescribed burning, which today exceeds in area what pre-refuge wildfires burned. (b) The national forests of the eleven western states stayed with suppression, and now confront a seemingly inexorable rise in wildfire. The figures for 1995 and 1996, when published, will probably exceed two million acres.

founding fire philosophy had been wrong. In a burst of institutional pride the Forest Service, in particular, sought to set things right.

In December 1995 the secretaries of interior and agriculture announced a joint federal policy that would, somehow, restore fire to a sane role in the public lands and shift responsibility for wildland fire protection from the federal government to cooperators, like the states, and to exurban communities. No one could say to what extent the reformation was really possible. The subsequent proposal to implement advocated as profound a reconstitution of federal fire (and public land) policy as welfare reform did for American social policy. Curiously both had originated in 1935 when the New Deal was in full flush and could argue that the federal government, and perhaps it alone, could ensure protection to both the American land and people; and both had come unglued in 1994. Each knew that the past no longer worked. Neither knew precisely how its projected future would evolve.

A Great Restoration

On a planet prone to combustion, removing controlled fire had only liberated the feral fire. Over most of America free-burning fire had gone wild—burning out of control and burning, preferentially, on wildlands. Paradoxically it was wild fire that thrived, while anthropogenic fire approached extinction. But could fire be "restored" to something like its former roles, if not its former dimensions? Or would it join condors and sand jays on special preserves, another exotic creature from a lost past? The evidence suggested that the answer was yes and no.

Global Trends

Some trends were global, part of planetary fire history from which the United States hardly stood exempt. Modernization was dividing the world into two great combustion moieties—one driven by the industrial combustion of fossil hydrocarbons, the other by the open burning of biomass. The technologies of the first systematically replaced those of the second.

Domestic fire. In the developed world domestic fire was gone. Where it survived, domiciled fire became typically no more than a house pet or ceremonial trophy. Functioning hearths were an anachronism. Fire for cooking, heat, light, and domestic crafts had vanished, leaving little more than candles and fake-log gas fireplaces in its stead. Even the burning of suburban lawns, garden debris, and autumnal leaves was increasingly prohibited or circumscribed.

Along with those lost household fires went a bred-in-the-bones familiarity with flame. Urban (and suburban, and exurban) America knew fire not as a daily routine or a reliable servant but as a destroyer of houses and a polluter of airsheds. Not to touch fire was among the first injunctions given to toddlers. Not to indulge in urban burning was among the strongest of adult proscriptions.

Agricultural fire. No less dramatic was the abrupt recession of agricultural burning. Rural America had exploited fire for endless purposes, not only in pioneering but to clear fields, to dispose of harvest refuse, to clean out ditches, to flush up pastures, to assist in auxiliary hunting and trapping, to prevent fuel buildups, and when wildfires came, to fight back with counterburns—an ancient register of fire practices. Prior to industrial agriculture, farming was a fire-fallow system, growing the fuels it would need to burn. Steadily, however, the traditional technology of open burning has also been replaced by the power of internal combustion and the distillation of fossil fallow. Tractors, chemical fertilizers, artificial pesticides and herbicides, all have broken the links that historically bound fallow to fire and that made burning indispensable to nearly all agricultural landscapes.

Besides, where the agricultural bordered the urban, local populations consider smoke a nuisance. The rural landscape is being recolonized by an exurban folk, many retired, for whom fire and smoke are an alien, unhealthy, and fearful presence. Not living on the land, they have not experienced personally the value of fire for land usage, and in fact, often do not want the land used other than for recreational and esthetic purposes. The only fires they experience are wildfires that savage subdivisions and submerge mountain valleys and scenic panoramas in smoke.

Wildland fire. In part these are global trends. In certain impoverished and overpopulated countries, especially in arid or semi-arid environments, the hunger for fuel wood and pasturage has driven fire out of the landscape and into (shrinking) hearths. But elsewhere the competition with industrial technology has removed fire from the landscape and placed it into furnaces and combustion chambers. The controlled burning of biomass continues to collapse as an ecological force.

But, perhaps paradoxically, fire remains and may even expand its dominion. The enduring fire, however, is too often wildfire. Agricultural lands abandoned as uneconomic in the face of global trade may sprout fuels that carry untended fire. (The northern rim of the Mediterranean is a good example.) Elsewhere, the passion for forest reservations and nature preserves—for wildlands, broadly defined—has fashioned a habitat for wildland

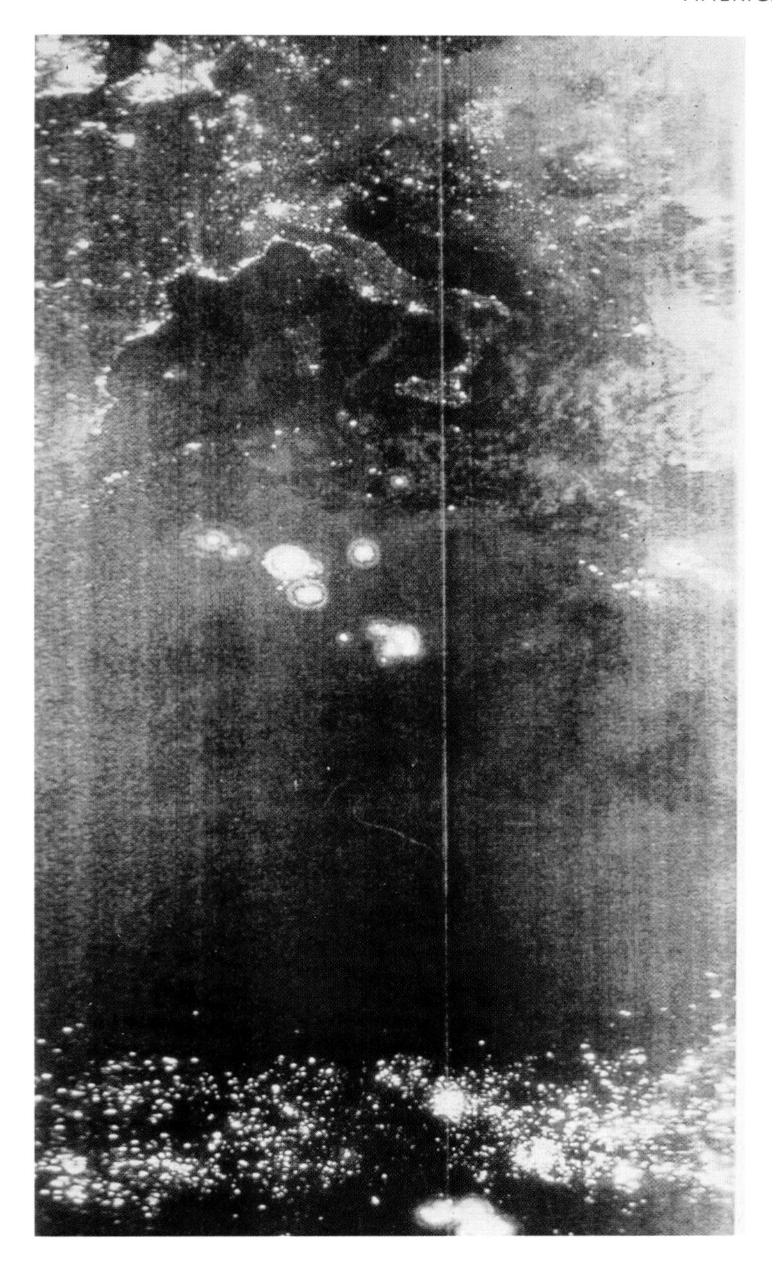

Figure 9. Evening satellite photo of western Europe and West Africa. The European glow results from industrial lighting; the speckled lights of Africa primarily result from burning vegetation. the sharp, double lighted rings come from natural gas flares. Defense Meteorological Satellite Program.

fire. For the most part, certainly in the United States, these fires are also wild. It is a pattern America shares with its colonial cognates like Canada and Australia. The future of fire is very much interdependent with the political future of such wildlands.

An ideological component to this containment persists as well, and it rests with another institutional context for fire. International environmentalism has demonized fire—so telegenic, so powerful when selectively broadcast—into a universal medium of ecological destruction. Nuclear winters, greenhouse summers, slashed-and-burned biodiversity, smoking rainforests, conflagrating urban borderlands, Kuwait oil-fields aflame, even the parboiled extinction of the dinosaurs, the iconography of fire is everywhere exploited to suggest catastrophe and shame, a literal hell on Earth. But by using the graphic imagery of fire to animate other agendas, environmentalism has created the sense of fire as itself intrinsically destructive, which is how it so often appears, in fact, to an urban clientele.

Nowhere does there exist an equivalent counter-image of fire as restorer, fire as purifier, fire as an ecological presence as fundamental as rain and sun. The sole exception, the renewal of fire in nature preserves, has only reinforced the sense of fire as a wild phenomenon, perhaps worth saving like wolves and grizzlies but only when confined to appropriate landscapes. The botched Yellowstone fires of 1988 mocked the ideology of natural regulation in which the invisible hand of nature's economy would balance fuel and flame. However revelatory the Yellowstone fires may have been regarding the potential place of fire in a natural order, their ecological effect proved largely negative. Prescribed fire became more difficult, more expensive, and more circumscribed. The off-site impacts were felt in Oregon, Minnesota, New Mexico, wherever prescribed fire was shut down, at least temporarily.

However majestic their symbolism, the successfully restored fires in places like Sequoia-Kings Canyon and Everglades national parks and the Selway-Bitterroot and Gila wildernesses could not compensate for plummeting burned area elsewhere. Continued recession marked the overall geography of fire. Perhaps less than 5 percent of the area that burned when Columbus sailed still burned, and that figure is probably high—no one knows. But like reefs revealed by a receding sea, the remaining flames became prominent by the shrinking lake of fire around them.

Special Landscapes: America

In the near term—that is, over the next century—these trends are unlikely to reverse. The fire mosaic of the United States is no longer, as it was in 1880, held together by the grout of rural fire. Instead it has splintered into a collage of special landscapes, each of which has demanded a unique response.

Wilderness fire. For a good twenty years, roughly 1970 to 1990, the question of fire in wilderness obsessed the American fire community. After the Wilderness Act (1964) and the Leopold Report (1963) for the National Park Service, the specter of fighting naturally ignited fires in nature preserves became intolerable. What had been an anomaly became an abomination. In 1967–68 the Park Service reformed its fire policy to reduce untrammeled fire suppression and reintroduce some benevolent fire. A decade later so did the Forest Service. (By the late 1980s nearly a fourth of the national forests were in gazetted wilderness.) Moreover, if fire was good for wilderness, it should be good everywhere. In a sense, it should be possible, through fire, to spread wilderness grace through otherwise fallen landscapes. Its alliance with wilderness almost certainly accounts for the enthusiasm with which prescribed burning became an acceptable philosophy of fire practice. Under its pressure fire control evolved into fire management.

But the philosophical euphoria that encouraged fire's restoration also often limited its character and application. *Natural* fire was the preferred, and at times exclusive, medium for burning. One result was the invention of the prescribed natural fire by which lightning-caused fires could be allowed to burn, subject to monitoring and a written prescription that spelled out place and properties. Other controlled burns were conceived as preliminaries to the full return of natural fire, poor surrogates (forced out of necessity), or as violations of the wilderness ideal and hence undesirable. The restoration of wilderness fire, while symbolically spectacular, remained small in area. In the overall geography of America, open burning continued to decline.

A less obvious but no less critical valence, however, was at work. Prescription burning demanded scientific research. Both prescribed fires and less singular suppression strategies (such as "confining" and "containing" fires) proposed to substitute fire knowledge for fireline power. The capacity to predict how a fire would behave and how it would affect an ecosystem became essential if prescribed burning was to be distinguished from let-burning, arson, or biotic vandalism, and such knowledge could arguably substitute for the sheer mechanical power of bulldozers, air tankers, and firefighters. Fire-by-

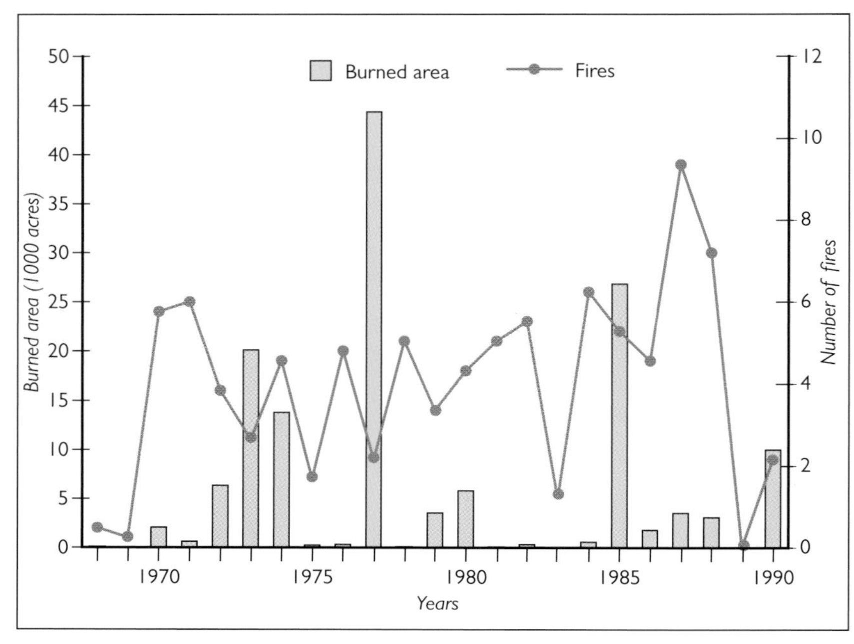
Burned area
Fires
Burned area (1000 acres)
Number of fires
Years
0
5
10
15
20
25
30
35
40
45
50
2
4
6
8
10
12
1970
1975
1980
1985
1990

[10a]

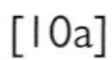

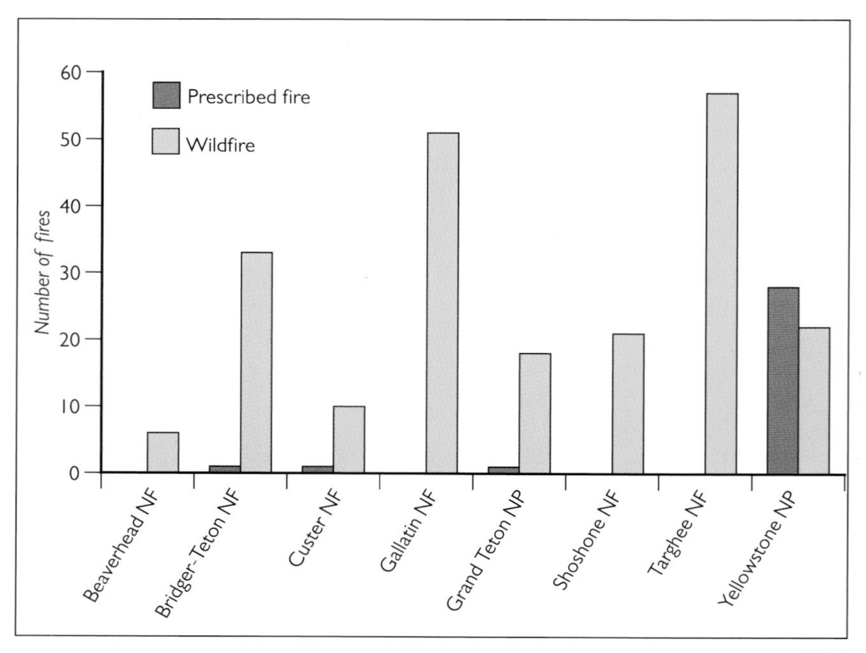
Prescribed fire
Wildfire
Number of fires
0
10
20
30
40
50
60
Beaverhead NF
Bridger-Teton NF
Custer NF
Gallatin NF
Grand Teton NP
Shoshone NF
Targhee NF
Yellowstone NP

[10b]

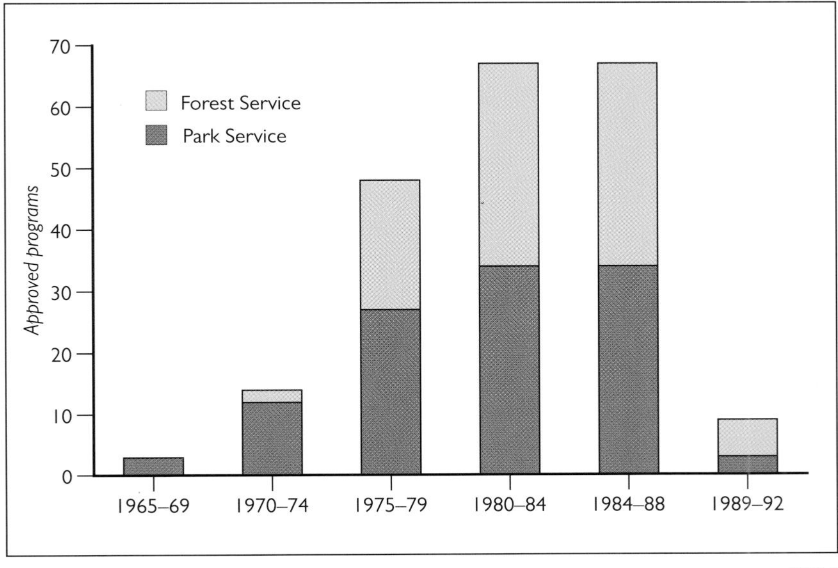

[10c]

Figure 10. Restoring fire: (a) Sequoia-Kings Canyon National Parks. In addition to prescribed natural fires, the parks have an active program of management burning, most spectacularly around and within sequoia groves. (b) Yellowstone National Park, 1988. The Greater Yellowstone Area experienced the same climatic conditions as the park but tolerated very few "natural" (or prescribed natural) fires. The park accepted them all until the fires reached politically unacceptable dimensions and then declared them and all subsequent starts as wildfires. Clearly the fire complex was the outcome of cultural decisions—what fires are good and bad, the presence of the park itself. Data from Wakimoto (1990). (c) The ecological consequences of the fires exceeded Yellowstone proper. By influencing institutions they shut down, temporarily, perhaps permanently, many natural fire programs, all of which had to cold-start after an interlude following the 1988 post-fire policy reviews.

prescription built on the hard pilings of an extraordinary outburst of fire science, well expressed by the creation of three dedicated fire laboratories by the Forest Service in the early 1960s.

Inevitably failures occurred. Prescribed burns went wild, prescribed natural fires escaped, benevolent burns smoked in cities and obscured natural wonders, prescribed fire killed firefighters, controlled burns incinerated critical habitats and the town of Mack Lake, Michigan, and perhaps most insidiously there was the fire that was never lit. Probably the era ended with the

Yellowstone fires of 1988. For much of the American public, the fires proved a revelation, a dramatic (if traumatic) introduction to fire ecology. But for the fire community, they formed an administrative fiasco, a $130 million testimony to a prescribed fire program that, in fact, lacked prescriptions.

The subsequent debate, however, became one of general fire policy rather than an inquiry into execution under existing policies. A review of federal policies compelled every unit to resubmit its fire plans. The national fire establishment had to cold-start their wilderness fire programs, and to do so at higher costs and under more rigorous regulation. Not all would succeed. This, finally, measured the real ecological effect of the Yellowstone fires. This and the fact that, while the problem of managing fires in wilderness remained, wilderness fire would no longer inform the agenda of the American fire community.

Intermix fire. Even as the smoke cleared over the Greater Yellowstone Area, another fire habitat clamored for special attention. The "wild" and the "developed" were more and more often abutting, intermingling in a landscape omelet, intergrowing into a tangled throng of ever-more-volatile fuels. Every region experienced the phenomenon, as abandoned farmland sprouted houses and woods, as suburbs and even metropolitan areas fostered a dense melange of trees and wooden structures, and especially as exurban strips clung along the borders of public lands like catclaw, or were stirred into public wildlands like chocolate chips in a cookie batter, ready for baking. As early as 1986, the federal agencies and National Fire Protection Association had launched a National Wildland/Urban Interface Initiative. By 1990 the intermix fire dominated fire practices and shaped the national discourse on fire policy.

The exurbanization of wildlands allowed communities to fall through jurisdictional cracks. All too often, no governmental body exercised authority for fire protection, and the fragmented communities sought none. Insurance companies were indifferent; zoning and building codes, absent. In essence, the rural landscape was being recolonized by an exurban population with urban values. Residents did not live off a rural economy; they did not graze, cut, plant, plow, burn, or otherwise manipulate the enveloping fuels; they expected that, as in cities, a fire service would protect them, even as they did nothing to create such a service. Where public wildlands lay adjacent, the federal land agencies served as a de facto fire department. More and more resources went into fighting the intermix fire, less and less into rehabilitating fire-famished biotas.

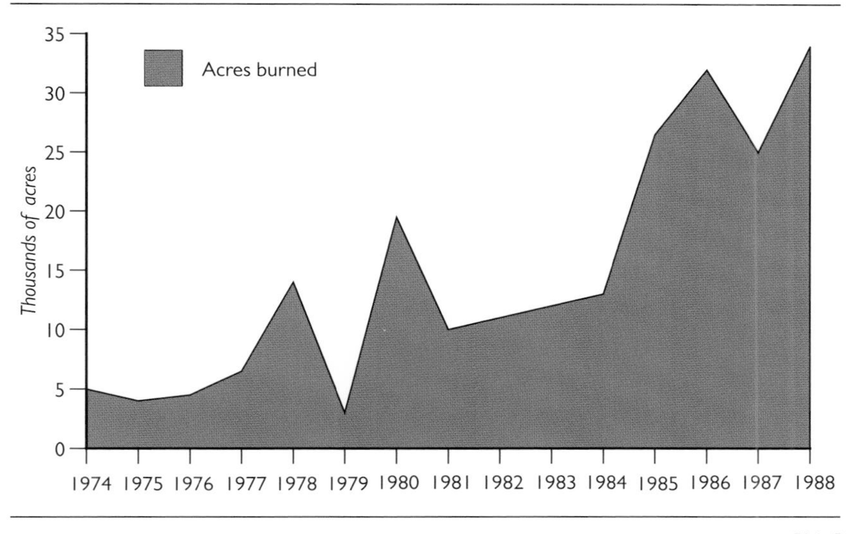

[11a]

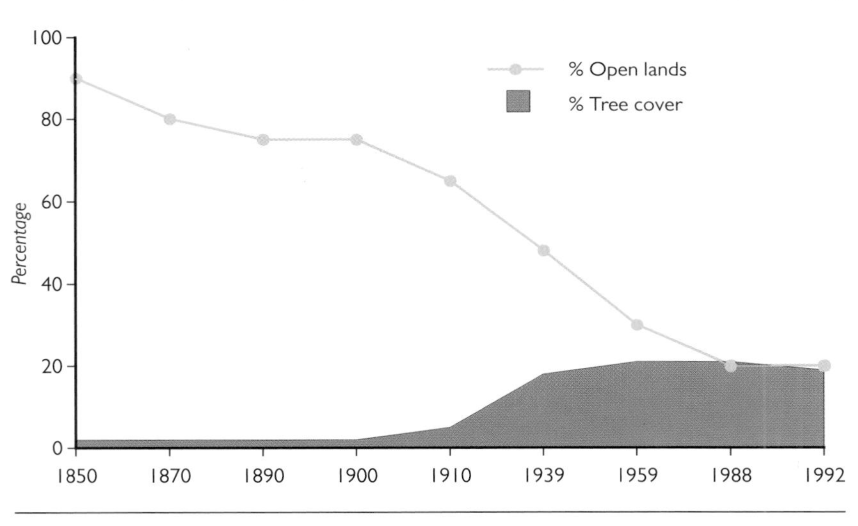

[11b]

Figure 11. The Fire This Time: The Intermix Milieu. (a) The rise in burned area in state and private lands, Colorado. (b) A conflagration cameo: the Oakland-East Bay fire, 1991. The loss of open area and an increase in woody fuels (trees and structures) is a metaphor for much of America; shortly after the trends crossed, the Berkeley Hills exploded. Data from Colorado State Forest Service; Nowak (1993).

The intermix fire scene complicated everything—ramming city and wildland together, mingling them through the medium of smoke, shrinking the domain of pure wildlands since each pocket of development created the need for a larger penumbra of protection. For decades American environmental thinking had polarized the country into wilderness and metropolis, like the ends of a bar magnet, and held everything else within their defining lines of force. But now the distance between those poles collapsed until they became almost one point. The rural buffer between them vanished. Intermix fire protection did not reside in firefighting but in creating sensible structures, defensible spaces, accessible entry and egress, over none of which the federal agencies had much say. The solution was political, and local; it resided with rural fire districts, county commissioners, and homeowner alliances, of which some species evolved in California, Arizona, Colorado, Florida, and elsewhere. Worse, perhaps, because the solutions were known, the incentive to invest in fire research faded. Reform required political will, not new knowledge.

The Forest Service, in particular, wanted to extricate itself from being a sole-source supplier of fire services throughout the country's exurbanizing forests and instead concentrate on the fire problems of the land itself. Certainly it remained a medium for what was becoming a second-order infrastructure for fire protection nationwide. But the Forest Service exercised little control over the social economics of exurban encroachment, and while it might promote more partners, it was unlikely that the agency would be allowed to pick up its shovels and drip torches and walk away into the woods.

Ecosystem management. That, however, was where the federal agencies truly wanted to be. The lands they held in public trust were, after a century, often a shambles. Forest health—grassland health, ecosystem health—had become a public scandal. Too many forests were overgrown, diseased, insect-infested, unattractive, prone to species losses, and vulnerable to catastrophic fire. Particularly at risk were those landscapes like ponderosa pine forests that had, in presettlement times, known frequent fire and now experienced vast, stand-replacing burns without historic precedent. Where early conservationists had rallied around the concept of a timber famine, modern environmentalists swarmed to the belief in a fire famine.

The policy reforms jointly issued in December 1995 sought to redress this imbalance. The agencies wanted to shift their emphasis from fire suppression to prescribed fire and to redefine the national agenda from an obsession with the intermix fire to a program of restoration burning. Fire suppression alone had not perverted the public lands, and fire use would not by itself restore them; but no proposed scheme to preserve healthy wildlands or rehabilitate degraded ones lacked a fire component. The fundamental problem was not to burn what had previously been unburned, but to determine, site by site, what constituted an appropriate fire regime. Some places would need more fire, some less, others a better mix. Pluralism had come to wildland fire management. Local needs would have to balance with national. But mistrust—not least for the lands' stewards like the Forest Service—made consensus elusive and fire practices polarizing.

Fire programs soon became a flashpoint for every controversy regarding the public lands. Everyone admitted to a fire crisis, but every group directed that alarm into its own agenda. Grazers wanted more grazing to reduce light fuels; loggers wanted more roads and more cutting to reduce heavy fuels; environmentalists wanted larger preserves to safeguard endangered species, lessen grazing, abolish logging; and so on. Even the so-called Timber Salvage Rider that in 1995 allowed timber harvesting on burns seemed to many environmentalists as an incentive to arson and a wedge by which to leverage logging into adjacent unburned forests. The fire that was common to all became a point of division. Early in the twentieth century, a fire crisis had united industry, government, and conservationists. The end-of-the-century's fire crisis seemingly drove them apart. Prescribed fire, in particular, lacked a vocal constituency; it had no one to argue that it was as much an intrinsic good as California condors or old-growth forests. Few groups proved willing to surrender some other good to make room for it, so in practice it became the residue left after all the contested controversies had been resolved. That wasn't much.

The disgraceful state of the public lands called into question, moreover, the very legitimacy of those lands. They were, after all, a political creation, not an indelible part of some environmental constitution. In the span of world history, they were rare, and those that had been created in the past, ephemeral. Yet what Americans recognize as a national fire problem is located in just such landscapes. "Wildland fire" is a creature of wildlands. Elsewhere the fires disappear into a tapestry of agricultural burning or rural fire protection or traditional foraging, hunting, and herding, slipping like shadows into the cultural landscapes they inhabit. Wildland fire burst forth because America

Figure 12. Firefight: a photographic sampler. Courtesy U.S. Forest Service.

(a) A crew around Mount Hood, Oregon, 1910

(b) CCC boys building fuelbreaks in Southern California

(c) The Cold War on fire, a staged exhibition of how fire control mechanized almost overnight following the Korean War

(d) Backfiring

possessed bounteous wildlands, a condition shared by only a handful of nations on Earth. Those lands had become the prime habitat for free-burning fire.

Some of those wildlands—nature reserves, national parks, wilderness—were probably safe from recommitment; the other public lands possibly not. Globally, the trend was toward devolution, privatization, and the transfer of authority to "local" powers, particularly where indigenous peoples were involved. None of America's cognate "fire powers" were spared. South Africa effectively privatized forestry, forest (and fire) research, and most of its forest firefighting. New Zealand disestablished its Forest Service and privatized its Forest Research Institute. The Canadian Forest Service, lacking public lands of its own to manage, began a rapid dissolution that would likely end in a significant degree of privatization. Australian Crown lands were being reconstituted from pastoral leases and (in some cases forests) to nature preserves and Aboriginal reserves, but there was no Commonwealth forestry service and only marginal national investment in bushfire research. By the mid-1990s, while Russia had not privatized its lands, it was leasing them, and its aerial fire protection program (the largest in the world prior to 1991) was in free-fall and its once mighty infrastructure for fire research was in such disarray that unpaid technicians busied themselves by planting potatoes on the grounds of the Russian Academy of Sciences' Laboratory of Forest Fire Research.

The United States was not immune to these afflictions. The three Forest Service fire labs imploded to one, the Intermountain Fire Sciences Laboratory at Missoula. In some form a degree of privatization would come—to fire research, to firefighting services other than aircraft and catering, to prescribed burning, to weather forecasts. So would forms of devolution, as the intermix fire drove federal fire management into partnerships with local fire districts and as air quality districts compelled prescribed burning to share airsheds with metropoli and coal-fired power plants. Throughout the American West, one cynic observed, the primary growth industries were casinos, toxic waste dumps, prisons, and summer homes. That was the larger cultural landscape with which federal fire management would have to exist. The larger environmental landscape was one in which industrial technologies for employing and circumscribing fire were aggressively substituting for open burning and in which international environmentalism (or its media allies) had, for the most part, demonized fire.

Controlled burning—so radiant philosophically—became in practice a prescription of last resort. The most likely scenario holds that prescribed fire will stabilize and even increase in special reserves but recede everywhere else. Open burning will survive only where it is a process, not a tool, or where it flourishes wild, an act of God, not a bureaucratic practice. Those privileged sites will be large, remote, and endowed with environmental values for which there are no real surrogates for free-burning fire. Outside them, the prospect appears that anthropogenic fire in America may join the melancholy register of Quaternary extinctions. Outside those preserves only wildfire may remain.

A Part for the Whole: Arizona

There were plenty of poster children available to advertise the problems and promises of the American fire scene. The Blue Mountains of Oregon were a paradigm of fire-related forest health problems. Yellowstone National Park revealed the failure of a natural-regulation ideology in fire management. California, Colorado, Michigan, and North Carolina symbolized the various avatars of the intermix fire. Florida emerged as a leader in controlled fire, developing a model Prescribed Burning Act in 1990 that was widely examined and cautiously emulated.

But as well as any place Arizona distilled the full spectrum of fire issues—epicenter for the lightning fire regime of North America, dominated by public lands (only 16 percent of the state's landmass was private), profoundly disturbed by the shock troops of fire exclusion (from grazing to fire suppression forces), bursting with in-migration and the economy of a metropolitan city-state. What happened elsewhere happened here, but all of what happened elsewhere happened here in some form. Let the part stand for the whole. Consider Arizona as synecdoche for America.

Wildfire. Throughout the 1990s wildfires savaged virtually every quasi-natural landscape. In 1990 the Dude Creek fire, kindled by lightning, blew up outside the town of Payson, burned over 28,000 acres and a fire crew of inmates (six died), and incinerated some exurban clusters sequestered tightly in the overstocked pine forest below the Mogollon Rim. Meanwhile the highway linking Phoenix to Payson experienced an acceleration of damaging fires as increased traffic, housing developments such as the exclusive Fountain Hills, and casinos on the Fort McDowell Reservation clawed into the land-

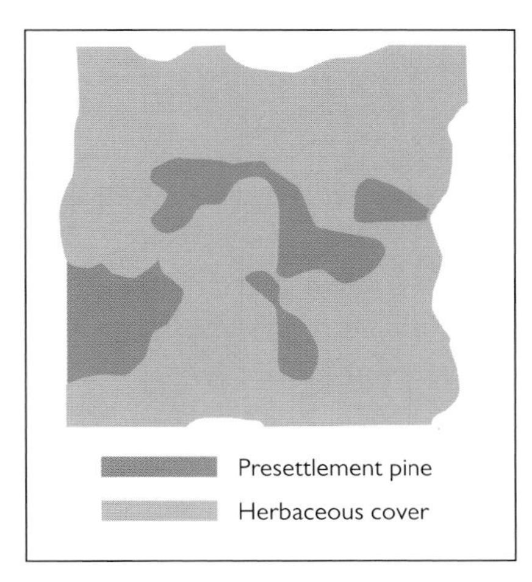

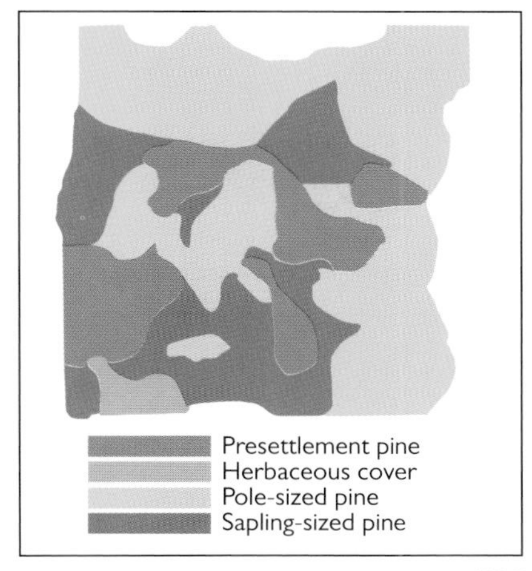

[13a]

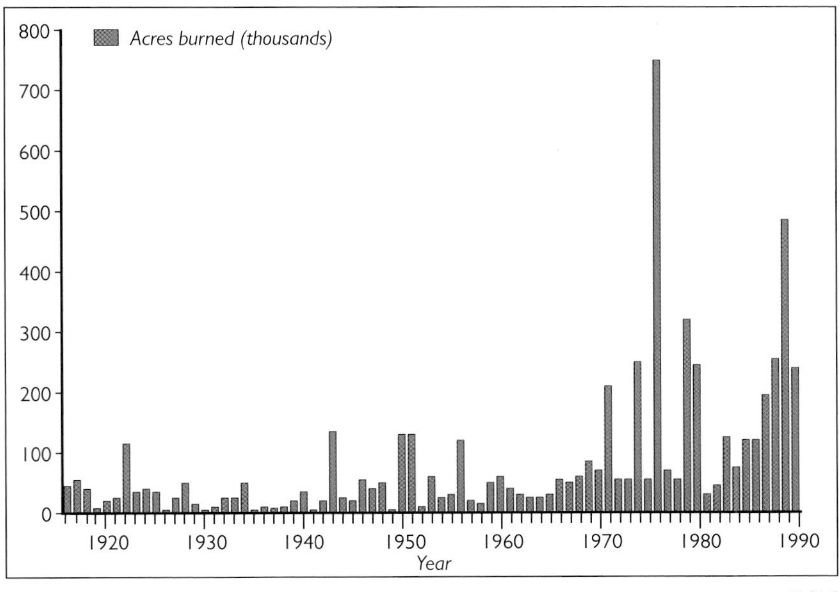

[13b]

Figure 13. Arizona example. (a) A century of fire exclusion around Flagstaff, Arizona encouraged an expansion in pole and sapling pine, mostly at the expense of herbaceous cover. In 1876 herbaceous cover is estimated at 83 percent; in 1990, at 4 percent. The dense thickets of young pine have become a major fuel hazard. Redrawn from maps by Wallace Covington. (b) Burned area in Arizona grows, powered by fuels and slowed or accelerated as climatic conditions permit. Data from U.S. Forest Service.

scape. Desert succulents and shrubs died; exotic pyrophytes like red brome invaded; the fire-catalyzed conversion spread out like a ship's wake to both sides of the Beeline Highway. In 1994 the Rattlesnake fire in the Chiricahua Mountains seared 25,000 acres and sent massive soil erosion down the valleys. In 1995 lightning ignited a blaze on the McDowell Mountains Park, a City of Scottsdale preserve only established by public vote a month previously in an effort to save some fragment of native vegetation from urban sprawl. The fires seared the Sonora Desert biota and terrified residents in the surrounding hills.

The next year, after a severe winter drought, fires moved up the mountains. On the Tonto National Forest, the Lone fire roared over 61,000 acres; indiscriminately burned degraded pasture, wildlife habitat, recreational trails, loose-soiled watershed, the Mazatzal Wilderness, and a Mexican spotted owl nest; threatened the hamlet of Punkin Center; and sent a cloud of smoke like sheet runoff into the Phoenix metropolitan area that for three days reduced Sky Harbor airport to instrument-only landings. To the south in the Coronado National Forest a fire broke out on Mount Graham, the scene of a bitter environmental controversy. A consortium of research universities, led by the University of Arizona, had proposed to enlarge a telescope complex on the summit until environmental groups, exploiting the Endangered Species Act, had thrown the issue into the courts. The fire was halted before it threatened the scope sites, but otherwise it burned indifferent to the imperatives of astronomy, congressional resolutions, court injunctions, Forest Service plans, the Environmental Protection Agency, or the wishes of the Mount Graham red squirrel. Meanwhile, the Horseshoe and Hochderffer fires outside pine-rimmed Flagstaff merged to consume 25,900 acres and panic urbanites. Then, lightning blasted a tree on the Esplanade of the western Grand Canyon into flame, a fire within the park's prescribed natural fire zone. The burn moved out of the Canyon at Bridger's Knoll and roared across 50,000 acres of the Kaibab National Forest, forcing the evacuation of the tourist facilities at Jacob Lake. The Bridger and Lone fires were the largest wildfires recorded in the state since World War II.

But that was not the bad news. The frightening statistic was that the average size of wildfires was increasing. Agencies freely confessed that they could no longer contain fires through sheer mechanical force, bureaucratic bluster, and the carte blanche monies of the emergency forest fire fund. The long-standing prediction by critics that the perverted fuels would create fires beyond technological control was proving correct. The public lands—most of the national forests and major parks—were simply closed to public access until the emergency passed. The Forest Service imported engines and crews from other, less endangered regions. When the monsoon storms arrived, they lit the skies with lightning, kindling more fires even as their delicious rains gradually extinguished the fire season. But while the climatic crisis passed, wildland fuels proliferated and exurban encroachment advanced and the public agencies admitted their incapacity, under extreme conditions, to keep pace.

Prescribed fire. The prescribed fire scene was likewise typical in theme, if somewhat exaggerated in size, from public lands elsewhere. Prescribed natural fires flourished intermittently at Grand Canyon and the Blue Primitive Area in the White Mountains. Slash burning cleared up logging debris. Juniper was chained and burned on the Hualapai Reservation; ponderosa pine was underburned on the Fort Apache Reservation. Broadcast burns for fuel reduction and habitat improvement crept and flashed over the grassy woodlands of the Santa Rita and related ranges. The Nature Conservancy sponsored a major prescribed fire program on its Gray's Ranch preserve. Aerial ignition dripped fire on the chaparral-clad Mazatzal Mountains in an effort to break up the continuity of decadent brush. For prescribed fire as for wild, the South continued to inscribe the fire triangle of the United States, but Arizona belonged in a second-tier ranking of states by the proportion of its protected lands that were controlled burned, and unlike the Northwest, most of these burns were not in slash piles.

From northern Arizona came a bold experiment to restore fire to public forests. Forestry professors at Northern Arizona University, building on research that documented the evolution of the region's perverted pine forests, proposed a regimen of cutting, grazing control, and burning that would reinstate something like the range of presettlement conditions. Prototype plots were prepared on the Fort Valley Experimental Forest located outside Flagstaff. In 1996 the concept scaled up to operational size at Mount Trumbull, a pine-clothed mountain secreted in the Arizona Strip. If the scheme succeeded, it would reduce fuels, renew a closed mill and rural economy (at Fredonia), rejuvenate a forest, and restore fire—and furnish a badly needed exemplar for the vast, similar landscapes throughout the western public lands.

Fire Critics. But if proponents for reform were present, so were critics.

Urban encroachment—in fact, as well as perception and values—was accelerating. Some 85 percent of the state's population resided in cities, almost two-thirds of that throng crowded into the Phoenix metropolitan area. All the state's loggers, millers, ranchers, and cowboys together would not fill an average metro high school. Suburban development pushed outward with the wild abandon of a dust storm, while exurbanites, led by retirees, reclaimed a rural landscape and converted ranches to summer homes.

They feared fire, and knew it only from urban settings. Few burned leaves on their lawns, or for that matter, any longer burned their lawns; few wanted prescribed fires in the public lands that constituted their exurban backyard. Above all there was the matter of air quality. The Phoenix metropolitan area especially was out of compliance with the Clean Air Act; too much carbon monoxide, too much ozone, too many particulates. Lawsuits were threatened; some were filed. While dust from desert roads and fields also contributed to what was becoming a perennial brown pall, the *causa causarum* was the automobile, and serious regulation of it was more or less anathema. Instead there were restrictions proposed for fireplace burning, and discussions about banning power lawn mowers and leaf blowers. There were concerns about possible penalties, including a loss of federal funds; there were alarms that a deteriorated airshed might slow growth; there were protests by organized (and well-heeled) retirement communities, ever a political power. When in the summer of 1996 highway construction crews on the Tonto National Forest burned away woody debris, the outcry made headlines. Meanwhile the United States was negotiating an international treaty to restrict greenhouse gas production, almost all of which came from combustion. It was not easy to explain why a million acres of old-growth forest burned in Yellowstone was an ecological wonder but a million acres burned in Brazil was a global tragedy. The competition for the atmosphere could only get worse.

Yet in the midst of all this the federal agencies were proposing to expand dramatically their prescribed burning. They would need to burn hundreds of thousands, even millions of acres; they would need to burn on this scale annually; and they would need to return periodically to reburn. The proposal seemed hallucinatory. Certainly, some burning could be wedged into favorable climatic cracks. Some would be staged in regions sufficiently remote that they would be, for practical purposes, invisible. After other needs were satisfied, some fire could be tolerated, burning assorted cultural slash, as it were. Where the values were compelling enough, some burning could simply be

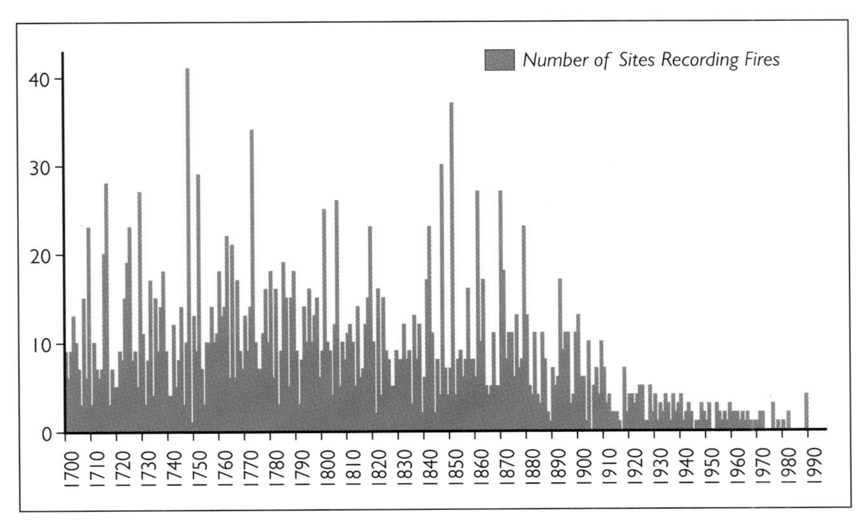

[14a]

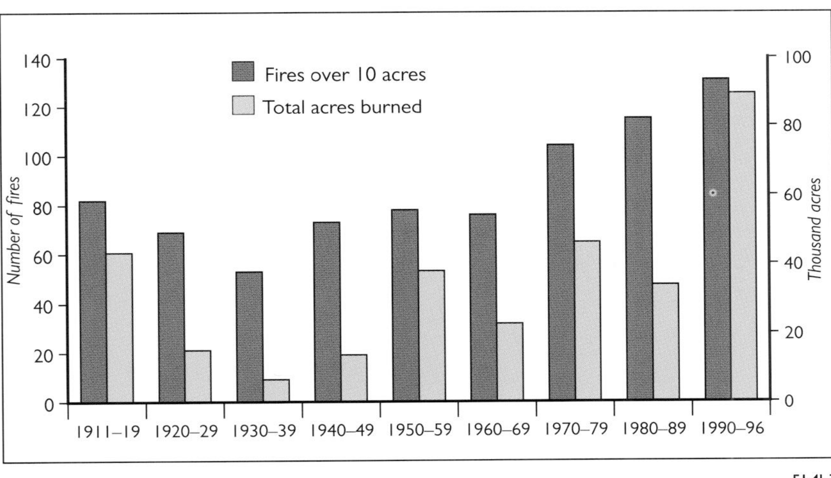

[14b]

Figure 14. Southwestern fire: a statistical profile. (a) The number of sites with a fire-scarred tree among sixty-three sites in the region. While there are exceptional years—typically the outcome of wet years succeeded by dry ones—the background fire load is relatively constant. The twentieth century, however, quickly and steadily suppressed that burning. Instead, as (b) reveals, after a decline in the magnitude and severity of burning, the postwar decades have witnessed a resurgence of wildfire, mostly in the form of large wildfires. Data sources: (a) Swetnam and Baisan (1996); (b) U.S. Forest Service.

forced through. Agencies could argue that the smoke would come, if not from controlled fire then from wildfire. But wildfire could not be sued, scorned, fired, denounced or ridiculed as human agents could.

It was as though the nominal keepers of Arizona's flame sat around a campfire, their backs to a fire (often one more virtual than real), each speaking to a separate constituency, each using those common flames to illuminate and animate other arguments peripheral to the fire itself. They declined to talk to one another across the flames, much less to make that central fire itself the object of their discourse. There was no clientele for free-burning fires as there was for Mexican spotted owls, red squirrels, and Aravaipa Creek. No advocacy group campaigned for fire as a unique ecological process whose extinction would distort the habitats of everything within its dominion. Arizonans, like most other Americans, had made their fuelbed and were prepared to lie in it.

The future of fire. A realist would say that reform on any significant scale was impossible. But history is not made by realists. The near prospect is that prescribed fire will expand selectively, as fire managers seek to transform their encircling firelines into fire cycles and as they kindle with fusees and helitorches a thousand points of light to cast back the ecological darkness. Free-burning fire would not reform whole landscapes—is not by itself capable of such transmutations—and would instead seek out and claim opportunistic niches and refugia, the same kind of sanctuaries that shield those plants, rocks, birds, and waters that stand outside an industrialized Earth. The gross geography of Arizona fire will continue to belong to the forces of industrial combustion.

That, for the indefinite future, would seem to be the fate of American fire overall.

Suggested Reading

Allen, Craig D., ed. "Fire Effects in Southwestern Forests." *Proceedings of the Second La Mesa Fire Symposium.* General Technical Report RM-286 (U.S. Forest Service, 1996).

Brown, James K. et al., tech. coords. *Proceedings: Fire in Wilderness and Parks Symposium,* General Technical Report INT-GTR-320 (U.S. Forest Service, 1995).

Chandler, Craig et al. *Fire in Forestry,* 2 vols. (Wiley, 1983).

Covington, W. Wallace et al. *Historical and Anticipated Changes in Forest Ecosystems of the Inland West of the United States* (Food Products Press, 1994).

Covington, W. Wallace and Pamela K. Wagner, eds., *Conference on Adaptive Ecosystem Restoration and Management: Restoration of Cordilleran Conifer Landscapes of North America.* General Technical Report RM-GTR-278 (U.S. Forest Service, 1996).

Crutzen, P. J. and J. G. Goldammer, eds. *Fire in the Environment. The Ecological, Atmospheric, and Climatic Importance of Vegetation Fires* (Wiley, 1993).

Dana, Samuel T., *Forest and Range Policy: Its Development in the United States* (McGraw Hill, 1956).

Goudsblom, Johan. *Fire and Civilization* (Penguin Press, 1992).

Holbrook, Stewart. *Burning an Empire* (Macmillan, 1944).

International Association of Wildland Fire. *Bibliography of Wildland Fire* (IAWF, 1996, updated).

Krammes, J. S., ed., *Effects of Fire Management of Southwestern Natural Resources. Proceedings of the Symposium,* General Technical Report RM-191 (U.S. Forest Service, 1990).

Langston, Nancy. *Forest Dreams, Forest Nightmares: The Paradox of Old Growth in the Inland West* (University of Washington Press, 1995).

Levine, Joel, ed. *Global Biomass Burning* (MIT Press, 1991).

Maclean, Norman. *Young Men and Fire* (University of Chicago Press, 1992).

Mooney, H.A. et al., tech. coords. *Fire Regimes and Ecosystem Properties,* General Technical Report WO-26 (U.S. Forest Service, 1981).

Nowak, D. J. "Historical Vegetation Change in Oakland and its Implications for Urban Forest Management," *Journal of Arboriculture* 19(5) (1993): 313–319.

Pyne, Stephen. *Fire in America: A Cultural History of Wildland and Rural Fire* (University of Washington Press, 1997; reprint).

______. *World Fire. The Culture of Fire on Earth* (Holt, 1995).

Pyne, Stephen, Patricia Andrews, and Richard Laven. *Introduction to Wildland Fire*, 2nd ed. (Wiley, 1996).

Report of the National Commission on Wildfire Disaster (Govt. Printing Office, 1994).

Sampson, R. Neil and David L. Adams, eds. *Assessing Forest Ecosystem Health in the Inland West* (Food Products Press, 1994).

Swetnam, Thomas W. and Christopher H. Baisan, "Historical Fire Regime Patterns in the Southwestern United States Since A.D. 1700." pp. 11–32, in Allen, ed., *Proceedings of the Second Le Mesa Fire Symposium*.

Tall Timbers Research Station. *Proceedings, Tall Timbers Fire Ecology Conferences*, Vols. 1–20 (Tall Timbers Research Station, 1962–1997).

U.S. Department of the Interior and Department of Agriculture. *Federal Wildland Fire Management. Policy and Program Review* (December 18, 1995).

Wakimoto, R. H. "The Yellowstone Fire of 1988: Natural Processes and National Policy," *Northwest Science 64* (1990): 239–242.

Wright, Henry A. and Arthur W. Bailey. *Fire Ecology— United States and Southern Canada* (Wiley, 1982).

About the Author

STEPHEN J. PYNE, b. 1949, is a professor of History at Arizona State University and a professional pyromantic. He specializes in environmental history and the history of exploration. But he has a particular fascination with the saga of fire, which stems from the fifteen years (1967–81) he spent with the North Rim Longshots at Grand Canyon and three subsequent years of fire planning for the Rocky Mountain Region of the National Park Service. We are, he observes, uniquely fire creatures on a uniquely fire planet.

All of his books derive from those experiences. One cluster, Cycle of Fire, is attempting to survey the history of humanity and fire. To date the Cycle consists of five volumes: *World Fire* (1995), *Fire in America* (1982), *Burning Bush* (1991), *The Ice* (1986), and *Vestal Fire*, a fire history of Europe, to be published in 1997. The University of Washington Press is publishing the collection as a set as part of its Weyerhaeuser Environmental Books.

A second suite deals with the Grand Canyon and exploration. Included are *Fire on the Rim* (1989), a memoir; *Grove Karl Gilbert* (1980); and several extended essays on the history of exploration. The third group embraces other fire studies, most notably, two editions of a text, *Introduction to Wildland Fire*, the revised edition co-authored by Patricia Andrews and Richard Laven.

Pyne has been at ASU since 1986 when he was hired as part of the charter faculty at ASU West, a branch campus; he transferred to ASU Main in 1996. He has received numerous awards, among them a MacArthur Fellowship, the Robert Kirsch Award from the Los Angeles Times for body-of-work contribution to American letters, and from the Forest History Society its Charles A. Weyerhaeuser book award, and Theodore Blegen award. He admits to having started and extinguished a fire on every continent.